ORNAMENTAL PHEASANTS
FOR BEGINNERS

by
Robert Deeley

Edited by Sara Roadnight
and Michael Roberts

Illustrated by Sara Roadnight

Diagrams by Michael Roberts

Please note: This book does not include
Peafowl and Junglefowl.

The cover photograph is a Himalayan Monal.

This book is dedicated to the
Wadham Collection of Pheasants
which was set up by Robert Deeley
and was sadly disbanded in 2006

Published by Gold Cockerel Books

ISBN 978 0947870 515

Acknowledgements

We would like to thank the following people
Mark Bechares
David Blank
Sujam Chatterjee
Lindsay Chrisp
Kenneth Fink
Francy Hermans [www.tragopan.fotopic.net]
David Heuclin
Zoe Hunter
Conor Keegan
Brian and Colin Moss
Dhiritiman Mukherjee
Jim Riddle
Michael Roberts
M. Vanden Wittenboer

This book would not have been
possible without their contributions.

Contents

INTRODUCTION

Interest in pheasants can be sparked off by the experience of finding a nest of warm olive coloured eggs in a hay field. You rescue them from the approaching farm machinery, carry them home and put them under a handy broody hen. She will take over and finish the job of the absent parent, and one day soon the eggs will 'pip' then hatch, and you will have your first pheasant chicks!

There can be few visitors to Bird Gardens or Zoos who are not impressed or amazed by the flamboyant plumage of ornamental pheasants; some people may even be tempted to think, I would really like some of those in my garden! Keeping ornamental pheasants can be a very rewarding hobby and they will certainly enhance your garden. Most of the birds described in this book are hardy and easy to feed and rear even though they originated in exotic places; and once you start keeping them, you will discover a completely new world of people and birds through organisations such as the World Pheasant Association.

Our aim in this book is to inform the beginner of the best methods of caring for ornamental pheasants, including details on aviaries, feeding, breeding and general health. We have divided the breeds into three different categories: beginners' pheasants, more challenging breeds, and difficult breeds, and have included a section on rare pheasants which are not available, so the book should appeal to pheasant keepers at all levels.

It is important to realise that some species of pheasant are on the verge of extinction in the wild, in which case captive breeding is vital to help conserve them; in fact, captive-reared stock from some endangered breeds have already been successfully introduced back into their natural habitat. So the breeding and rearing of most ornamentals is pure conservation and is helping to keep alive certain species which would undoubtedly have died out without it.

'Peacocks Past and Present' in the Gold Cockerel Series is aimed at anyone interested in keeping peafowl. A book on Junglefowl will follow in due course.

THE PHEASANT FAMILY

Before we go any further we need to look at the various groups or genera of pheasants of which there are 16:

GENUS

1	Ithaginis	Blood pheasants.
2)	Tragopan	Tragopans: Western, Satyr, Blyth's, Temminck's and Cabot's.
3)	Pucrasia	Koklass.
4)	Lophophorus	Monals: Himalayan, Chinese and Sclater's.
5)	Gallus	Junglefowls: Red, Green, La Fayette's and Sonnerat's.
6)	Lophura	Gallo pheasants: Kalij, Silver, Imperial, Edward's, Swinhoe's, Salvadori's, Malaysian Crestless Fireback, Bornean Crested Fireback, Siamese Fireback, Vieillot's Crested Fireback and Bulwer's Wattled Pheasant.
7)	Crossoptilon	Eared-Pheasants: White, Brown and Blue Eared-Pheasants.
8)	Catreus	Cheer Pheasants.
9)	Syrmaticus	Long-Tailed Pheasants: Elliot's, Hume's Bartailed, Mikado, Copper and Reeves.
10)	Phasianus	True Pheasants: Melanistic, Ringneck, etc.
11)	Chrysolophus	Ruffed Pheasants: Golden and Lady Amherst's.
12)	Polyplectron	Peacock Pheasants: Bronze-tailed, Rothschild's, Germain's, Grey, Malaysian and Palawan.
13)	Rheinartia	Crested Argus.
14)	Argusianus	Great Argus.
15)	Pavo	Peafowl: Indian or Blue, Green Peafowl.
16)	Afropavo	Congo Peacock.

There are 48 species of pheasant and their original habitat includes areas stretching from the eastern coast of the Black Sea across to and including Asia, Japan, Formosa and the Phillipines. The exception is the Congo Pheasant which comes from Africa.

PLEASE NOTE - This book does not deal with any of the Peafowl or Junglefowl. Peafowl are covered in 'Peafowl Past and Present' in the Gold Cockerel Series and a book about Junglefowl will follow in due course.

Sara Roadnight

BEGINNERS' BREEDS

We recommend the following breeds for beginners as these birds are freely available from collections or breeders. Aviaries are discussed in detail in a separate chapter.

The Golden Pheasant (Chrysolophus pictus)

This breed comes from central China where it lives in bamboo plantations and scrubland. It is easy to keep and extremely hardy, often preferring to roost out in the aviary at night. The male has a bright gold feathered crest with a black barred orange ruff or cape which hides most of his face and beak when he displays during courtship. True Golden Pheasants are becoming difficult to find as there are several mutations including lemon or yellow, and they cross readily with the Lady Amherst Pheasant. Female Golden Pheasants are a dull brown with black markings. The poults look like the females for the first year, with the males showing just a hint of red on their necks and developing their full plumage in their second year. The females lay 6 to 12 eggs in February and March of the same year.
Aviary size: Small.

Pure Golden Pheasant.

Lemon or yellow mutation.

The Silver Pheasant (Lophura nycthemera nycthemera)

This is the true Silver Pheasant which comes from Southern China. Delacour mentions 13 sub-species, one of which, the Lewis's (Lophura nycthemera lewisi) I have bred although it is sometimes a shy breeder. It is hardy, easy to keep and becomes very tame, but can develop a bad egg eating habit. The females will sit on their eggs and make excellent mothers. The male has a green mantle and a blue crest, and his silver-grey feathers are all delicately double-laced in black. The breast is a striking bluish purple, and the legs and face are red. It takes two years for the males to attain their full adult plumage. The females lay about 5 eggs in March of their second year.

Aviary size: Medium

Lewis's Silver Pheasant.

Lady Amherst's Pheasant (Chrysolophus amherstiae)
This breed comes from South central and Western China and is another stunning and easy breed to keep. The males have a scarlet crest, bright green and blue wings which blend into a whitish grey breast, and a beautiful long grey tail heavily barred with chestnut under coverts. They develop their full adult plumage in their second year. The females lay between 5 and 12 eggs in April of their second year. It can be difficult to find pure Lady Amherst's Pheasants as many have been crossed with the Golden Pheasant.
Aviary size: Small

True Pheasants (Phasianus)

These are game bird pheasants which originated on the eastern shores of the Black Sea and across to Asia. Before they are dismissed as Ringnecks they deserve a closer look; the Americans and Germans are showing a lot of interest in them now. There are probably about 30 variants, many beautifully coloured such as the Green versicolour, Formosan and Black melanistic. They are very hardy and easy to keep. The male birds attain their full adult plumage in their first year and the females lay up to 30 eggs in March of that year.

Aviary size: Medium to large.

MORE CHALLENGING BREEDS

You have to be a little more experienced if you are thinking of buying any of these breeds. They all need medium to large aviaries, and because some of them are rare and quite expensive they require a greater attention to detail in their care and upkeep.

The Elliot's Pheasant (Syrmaticus ellioti)
This bird comes from Eastern China and is a long tailed breed. It is hardy and easy to keep but is much rarer than the Reeves Pheasant and shares its rather unpleasant spiteful trait. For this reason the aviary must be well planted so that the hens can conceal themselves when necessary. The males are most striking birds with long chestnut barred grey tails; they attain their full adult plumage in their first year and the hens lay about 7 eggs in March of the same year.
Aviary size: Medium to large

The Reeves Pheasant (Syrmaticus reevesi)

This is a hardy breed which comes from the wooded mountains of central North China. The male is a magnificent bird with a black and white head, and russet, yellow and white feathers laced with black on his body. His tail is white with black bars and can grow to 1.5 meters in length which means these birds must have long and large aviaries. There is one drawback with this breed: the males can be very spiteful, not only to their hens and other males but humans as well. The chicks also have this trait and should be reared separately. The aggressive nature of these pheasants would enable them to live quite well in the wild in the U.K. although it would be illegal to release them into the wild. They acquire their full adult plumage in their first year and the hens lay between 8 and 14 eggs in April of that year.

Aviary size: Long and large

Mikado Pheasant (Syrmaticus mikado)

This is a hardy breed which comes from the densely forested mountains of Taiwan. It is a long tailed species, mainly metallic blue-black in colour with greenish tinges and two disinctive white bars across the wing coverts, rump and tail. The males develop their full adult plumage during their first year and the hens begin to lay, usually about 7 to 10 eggs, also in their first year.

Aviary size: Medium to large

Hume's Bar-tailed Pheasant (Syrmaticus humiae humiae)
This bird comes from North East India and Northern Burma and is a member of the long tailed genus Syrmaticus. It has beautiful markings and a black barred tail which it fans outwards when it walks. The cock birds develop their full adult plumage during their first year and the hens lay between 5 and 11 eggs in April of that year.
Aviary size: Medium to large

Monal Pheasant (Lophophorus)

This breed comes from the mountains of the Himalayan range in an area stretching from Afghanistan to Bhutan. There are three subspecies:

Himalayan Monal (Lophophorus impeyanus)

Chinese Monal (Lophophorus ihuysi)

Sclater's Monal (Lophophorus sclateri)

Himalayan Monals have amazing metallic colours, blues, greens, bronze and black. They develop their full adult plumage during their second year. They are frequently found in zoos and collections because they are so decorative. They are hardy birds but do like to dig so you must think carefully about the planting in their aviary. The hens lay 5 to 8 eggs in April of their second year.

Aviary size: Medium

Cock displaying to hen.

16

Swinhoe's Pheasant (Lophura swinhoei)

This breed comes from Taiwan and is fairly easy to keep. It is quite a large bird with a white crest, white nape to the neck and large white feathers in the tail. The males attain their full adult plumage during their second year and the hens start to lay, usually half to a dozen eggs, in March of the second year.

Aviary size: Small to medium

This bird has a slightly damaged tail.

17

Kalij Pheasant (Lophura leucomelana)

This breed comes from an area stretching from Pakistan through Northern India and into Bangladesh. There are nine subspecies of this genus:

Nepal Kalij (L.l. leucomelana)
White Crested Kalij (L.l. hamiltoni)
Black Kalij (L.l. moffitti)
Black Breasted or Horsefield's Kalij (L.l. lathami)
Black Backed Kalij (L.l. melanota)
Lineated Kalij (L.l. lineata)
Crawfurd's Kalij (L.l. crawfurdi)
Oate's Kalij (L.l. oatesi)
William's Kalij (L.l. williamsi)

They are hardy as they come from the forested foothills of the Himalayas. The males attain their full adult plumage during their first year and the hens can lay up to 15 eggs in April of the same year.
Aviary size: Medium to large.

Horsefield's Kalij.

Lineated Kalij.

White Crested Kalij.

Nepal Kalij.

The Edward's Pheasant (Lophura edwardsi)

This breed is a native of Laos and Vietnam and is one of the large group of pheasants covered by the Lophura genus. It used to be quite rare but is making a wonderful comeback. This small glossy purple bird is quiet and shy; it has green wing coverts, a white crest and a bright red face and legs; it develops its full adult plumage during its first year. The hens are buffy brown with delicate black markings; they lay about half a dozen eggs in their first year.

Aviary size: Medium

Imperial Pheasant (Lophura Imperialis)

Discovered by Jean Delacour in 1923 in the province of Bong Hoi, North Vietnam.

A pair of these birds was sent to Monsieur Delacour in Cieres north of Rouen, where, incidently, his garden is worth a visit if you are passing that way. He bred from them, but there are doubts in some quarters as to whether the breed was pure. The male is similar to an Edward's Pheasant but has a black crest, and the female resembles a female Silver Pheasant. Furthermore the Edward's and the Silver do cross and produce fertile offspring.

19

Eared-Pheasants (Crossoptilon)

These are all digging pheasants so their aviaries must have plastic netting laid over the grass to protect it (see end of section on Aviary Construction). When rearing 2 to 3 day old Eared-Pheasant chicks be aware of the fact that they have a tendancy to eat each others toes so keep an eye on them and try to distract them! A unique feature of these pheasants is that the males and females have the same plumage.

White Eared-Pheasant (Crossoptilon crossoptilon crossoptilon)

These pheasants come from Tibet and Western Szechuan in China. There are two sub-species, the Tibetan Crossoptilon crossoptilon drouyni which is white, and Dolan's Crossoptilon crossoptilon dolani which is white with grey wings. Unlike the other species of Eared-Pheasants these have no ear tufts. They are large hardy pheasants which love to dig so you need to plan the planting of their aviary with this in mind. They can be very aggressive but this is not always the case. The males acquire their full adult plumage in their first year but are not fertile until their second year; the females start to lay in April of their first year, usually about half a dozen eggs, but these will not be fertile until the second year. Aviary size: Large and grassy.

Tibetan White Eared-Pheasant

*Szechuan White
Eared-Pheasant*

Brown Eared-Pheasant (Crossoptilon mantchuricum)

These hardy pheasants come from the mountain forests of North China and are very rewarding to keep as they are so friendly and talkative and become very tame. The body feathers are brown and the tail feathers white with brown at the ends; there are twenty two feathers in the tail which makes it look rather heavy. Like all Eared-Pheasants, these birds are very fond of digging, so be aware of this. They acquire their full adult plumage in their first year, and the hens lay about 8 eggs in April but these are rarely fertile until the second year.

Aviary size: Large and grassy.

Blue Eared-Pheasant (Crossoptilon auritum)

This species comes from central North China. It is a large bluey green bird with white ear tufts and some white feathers in the tail. Like all Eared-Pheasants these birds love digging so plan their aviary with this in mind. They attain their full adult plumage in their first year and the hens start to lay, usually about 8 eggs, in April of that year but are rarely fertile until the next year.

Aviary size: Large and grassy.

DIFFICULT BREEDS

The pheasants in this classification are included for various reasons:
    a) they have special needs ie heating, particular foods etc.
    b) there are very few, if any in captivity
    c) they are in-bred
    d) they hybridise easily
    e) they are sometimes very expensive
but they can be the most spectacular and beautiful birds to keep in terms of colour.

The Koklass Pheasant (Pucrasia macrolopha)
There are ten races within this family which comes from the foothills of the Himalayas, from Afganistan through to India, Nepal and north eastern parts of Tibet and China. Although they inhabit a vast area they have proved difficult to keep in captivity because of their susceptibility to parasitic infection. They have to be kept either in a large grassy aviary (up to 800 sq ft) underlaid with wire mesh to prevent parasitic infection, or just on wire mesh alone, with regular doses of Flubenvet to prevent a build up of internal parasites; for external parasites you will have to use Novamectin or Ivamectin. They can lay up to 12 eggs in April of their first year when they attain their full adult plumage. They require large quantities of green foodstuffs such as grass and lucerne.
Aviary size: Large and grassy.

Tragopans

There are five sub-species within this family which come from various regions in the foothills of the Himalayas at quite high altitudes, 6,000 to 10,000ft with the Cabot at rather lower altitudes of 3,000 to 5,000ft. They are undoubtedly one of the most beautiful and colourful pheasants and are very much sought after. A great deal of care and, I feel, some luck is needed when breeding these birds, although their numbers have increased thanks to A.I. and the good work of the World Pheasant Association. Unfortunately the Temminck's readily crosses with the Satyr and Cabot's and this has led to a certain number of hybrids on the market. Conversely, because of the low numbers of certain other Tragopans, particularly the Blyth's, Cabot's and Western, the residue stock from early importations is becoming very inbred and genetically weak. These pheasants need large aviaries and nest off the ground, normally in baskets or open nest boxes. Their foodstuff is mainly vegetarian, including fruit and berries.

Satyr

Temminck's

Cabot's

Blyth's

Western

24

Satyr Tragopan (Tragopan satyra)

This is the commonest and most prolific of the family. It lives in the rhododendron forests of India, Nepal, Sikkim, Bhutan and Arunachal Pradesh. The adult cock is bright red with white spots and black and brown markings which are most striking when he is in full display. The female is a dull brown in contrast with lighter underparts mottled with black and a brown barred tail. She lays 2 to 4 eggs in April of her second year when the birds attain their full adult plumage.

Aviary size: Large.

Temminck's Tragopan (Tragopan temmincki)

This pheasant lives in the thick evergreen forests of North East Assam, Arunachal Pradesh and North East China. It has bred well in captivity but you must take care to check their purity when buying these birds because, as we have already mentioned, they cross very readily with Satyr and Cabot's Tragopans. These birds develop their full adult plumage in the second year and the hens lay 6 to 8 eggs in April of that year. Aviary size: Large.

Cabot's Tragopan (Tragopan caboti)

These are found in the mountain forests of South East China. The European stock is fearfully inbred but new stock has been released from China, and hopes are rising for these birds. They are very beautiful with mellow cream and orange colouring. In their second year they develop their full adult plumage and the hens start to lay, but only 2 to 4 eggs in a clutch.

Aviary size: Large

Blood Pheasant (Ithaginis cruentus)
There are 11 subspecies of this breed which is the smallest of all pheasants being about the size of a French partridge. It has a huge range along the Eastern side of the Himalayas through Nepal, Tibet, North Burma and into North West China. It lives high up in the mountains at about 14,000ft in the summer and comes down to about 11,000ft in winter. (As a result of living at such high altitudes this pheasant is extremely vunerable to parasitic infections when it is moved to a more temperate climate so it is important to be aware of this.) It lives mainly in conifer forests but does frequent deciduous woods as well. The females lay in May of their first year when they have their full adult plumage; there are normally 6 to 10 eggs in a clutch but sometimes more.
Aviary size: Large.

Firebacks

These pheasants take their name from the cock bird: when he is displaying he stands on his tiptoes, whirs his wings and exposes a bright orangey yellow patch of feathers on his lower back or rump. They are beautiful birds which often become quite tame, but the cock can be aggresive to the female and require seperation to neighbouring accomodation. During the breeding season he should be allowed in to mate with her each time she lays an egg then taken out afterwards; you need a clever system of runs and popholes to achieve this without causing your birds too much stress. (These pheasants must be bred in pairs only.) The hens lay 5 to 8 eggs in their third year; they sometimes start in their second year but are rarely fertile then. The chicks are shy feeders requiring small mealworms with their pheasant crumbs and the adults also need plenty of insects such as mealworms in their diet as well as pheasant pellets. The aviaries must be large, well planted and high as the birds roost at 8 to 10 ft, and there should to be a protected heated area for them in the winter. These birds have extremely sharp spurs so gloves are essential when you handle them.

Siamese Fireback cock wing whirring

Siamese Fireback (Lophura diardi)

These pheasants are found in Vietnam and Eastern Thailand where they live in dense lowland forests and bamboo thickets. They adapt well to the English climate inspite of coming from a semi tropical part of the world, but they do need a draught/wind free enclosure to protect them in cold weather. One disadvantage is that they are quite susceptible to frosted toes. They take three years to mature and breed well from then on and they are a good Fireback for a beginner to start with. They develop their full adult plumage in their first year although it is not as bright as it will become in a year or two. The cock bird is a handsome fellow with a greyish upper body marked with wavy black lines, and broad dark green tail feathers. The female is chestnut brown with black and white wavy bands on her wings. She lays 4 to 8 eggs in her third year.

Aviary size: Large.

30

Malaysian Crestless Fireback (Lophura erythrophthalma)

There is a Bornean sub-species Lophura erythrophthalma pyronata. These pheasants are found in the low-lying rain forests of Western Sumatra. The cock bird has a red face with blue wings and shoulders merging into a black body. The back is dark cinnamon in colour and the tail light cinnamon. The hens breed in their second year and lay 4 to 6 eggs in a clutch. These pheasants require heated accomodation for the winter.

Aviary size: Large.

Malaysian Crestless male.

Bornean Crestless male.

Vieillot's Crested Fireback (Lophura ignita rufa)

These pheasants are to be found on the Malay Peninsular and most of the island of Sumatra. The outstanding feature of this bird is the crest of feathers on its head similar to a peacock's. The body is purple striped with white spangling on the breast, it has a bright scarlet back, a pale blue face and a tail which is white on top and greenish blue below. This Fireback is probably the most common of the three in captivity. It requires heat in the winter. The hens occasionally lay in their second year but normally start in their third, laying 3 to 8 eggs.
Aviary size: Large.

Bornean Crested Fireback (Lophura ignita)
These pheasants come from South Borneo and Java and are delightful birds which most people would be keen to have in their collections. They need well planted aviaries and heat in the winter months. They are large birds and the males are dark metallic blue with russet red on their breasts and yellow feathers in their tails; they have extraordinary bright blue wattles which become very prominent when they are excited. The hens sometimes breed in their second year but normally begin in their third, laying 3 to 8 eggs.
Aviary size: Large.

Salvadori's Pheasant (Lophura inornata)

This pheasant comes from the rain forests of Southern Sumatra and is rarely found in collections. The male is dark blue with a red face and short tail, while the female is reddish brown and buff with finely spotted feathers. She breeds in her second year and lays 2 to 4 eggs in a clutch. These birds need heated accomodation for the winter.

Aviary size: Large.

Bulwer's Wattled Pheasant (Lophura bulweri)
This pheasant comes from Borneo. It is bigger then the Bornean Crested Fireback and has a large blue black body and white tail; its vivid light blue wattles enlarge during courtship. Very few are seen in captivity. The hens breed in their second year and lay 3 to 6 eggs in a clutch. These birds need heated accomodation for the winter.
Aviary size: Large

Vietnamese Pheasant (Lophura hatinhensis)

This pheasant is from Central Vietnam. It was only discovered in 1975 and is sometimes called Vo Quy's Pheasant after the man who found it. The male is blue-black with a red face and white central tail feathers. It is quite similar to the Edward's Pheasant, differing only in the white tail feathers; the hens lay 4 to 6 eggs in a clutch.

Aviary size: Medium.

Peacock Pheasants (Polyplectron)

There are six sub-species within this family which is perhaps the noisiest of all the pheasants. They come from a huge area which stretches from the Eastern Himalayas, Burma and South China to the island of Hainan, Vietnam, Laos, Malaysia, Sumatra, Borneo and the island of Palawan in the Phillipines. They are called Peacock Pheasants because most of them have feathers marked with an eye or ocellus like a peacock. Some of the breeds are hardier than others but they all require heated areas for cold days and nights. They can be kept in medium sized aviaries but these must be well planted. Their diet is varied ranging from pheasant pellets, wheat and cracked peanuts to berries, fruit, mealworms and minced meat. The young chicks are shy feeders to begin with and do best if they are reared with others which feed readily and will encourage

them. The hens nest in raised nest boxes although they have been known to lay on the ground; they produce only two eggs in a clutch but sometimes three or four clutches in a season. They attain their adult plumage in their second year. The male birds have one, two or even three spurs on their long legs so you should take care when handling them.

The Grey Peacock Pheasant (Polyplectron bicalcaratum)

This pheasant is also called the Chinquis Pheasant and is the national bird of Myanmar (Burma). The species can be found in a huge area stretching from Sikkim, Burma, North and West Thailand, North Laos and North Vietnam to South China and the island of Hainan. There are five sub-species: the Himalayan, the Burmese, the Lowe's, the Ghigi's and the Hainan. The first four are fairly similar in colour, being more grey in the Western side of the territory and more brown in the Eastern side. These pheasants usually make good mothers but they do need heated quarters for the winter months. The male is much larger than the hen. They attain their full adult plumage in their second year and the hens lay two eggs per clutch.

Aviary size: Medium.

Germain's Peacock Pheasant (Polyplectron germaini)

This species comes from South Vietnam where it lives in damp, fairly low altitude forests rising no higher than 3,500ft. These shy birds are less colourful than the Grey Peacock Pheasants and have no ruff or crest. They require a heated area for the winter or when it is cold and windy. They attain their full adult plumage in their second year and lay two eggs in a clutch.

Aviary size: Medium.

Bronze-Tailed Peacock Pheasant (Polyplectron chalcuran)

This species is to be found in Sumatra and is one of the smallest of all

the pheasants. It is a dull brown colour with narrow barring across the feathers; the tail ends have metallic bluey purple areas near the tips, and neither male nor female has any ocelli on their feathers. They require a heated area for cold weather. They attain their full adult plumage in their second year and the hens lay two eggs per clutch. Aviary size: Medium.

Malaysian Peacock Pheasant (Polyplectron malaceuse)

This species is found in the hill country of Malaysia along with a sub-species called the Bornean Peacock Pheasant (Polyplectron malaceuse schleiermacheri) which is found in South East Borneo; this sub-species is very rare and not seen in captivity, although the Malaysian Peacock Pheasant is seen in collections but needs a heated area for the winter months as the hens lay in December and January. They produce only one egg at a time which is why they are uncommon in captivity.
Aviary size: Large.

Palawan Peacock Pheasant (Polyplectron emphanum)

This species comes from the Palawan Islands on the Western side of the Phillipines. It is considered to be the most attractive of the Peacock pheasants which has led to its decline in the wild, although there are at

present a fair number in captivity. They need heated accomodation for the winter months. The male Palawan has metallic blue on his wings and coverts and a large blue crest. He displays his tail much like a turkey. The hens lay a clutch of 2 eggs in March with further clutches into the summer months; some hens will sit on their own eggs. The chicks are shy feeders and need encouraging with live meal worms to get them started on pheasant crumbs.

Aviary size: Medium.

Rothschild's Peacock Pheasant (Polyplectron inopinatum)
Also known as the Mountain Peacock Pheasant.
This species comes from the central mountainous area of Malaysia, and is another colourful bird from this family of pheasants. It is also one of the rarer Peacock Pheasants, only a few having been reared in captivity. They require a heated area for cold days and the winter months. The hens will nest in raised baskets as well as down on the ground, laying 2 eggs in each clutch.
Aviary size: Medium to large.

The Great Argus

There are two sub-species of Great Argus, one from Malaysia and Sumatra (Argusianus argus argus) and the other from Borneo (Argusianus argus grayi). The Malaysian species is more common both in the wild and captivity. The Great Argus is quite a noisy bird and is one of the largest of all pheasants, measuring nearly 2 metres or over 6ft long. The male produces one of the most spectacular displays during the mating season and needs a good big clearing at least 5m square in the aviary in which to perform when he is attracting a female. A good sized heated area is essential for the winter. Great Argus Pheasants take three years to attain their full plumage, and the female lays 2 eggs in a clutch. Their diet is mixed and should include live mealworms or maggots, berries, wheat and pheasant pellets.

Aviary size: Large and high.

Great Argus displaying.

45

Cheer Pheasant (Catreus wallichii)

This bird is found on the steep craggy hillsides of the Western Himalayas and through to Pakistan, India and Nepal. It is not seen in collections very often as it is rather noisy and not very 'showy'. The plumage is a dusky grey brown with fine black and white barring. These pheasants are great diggers and need large aviaries or smaller ones with sand floors. They attain their adult plumage in their first year and the hens lay 8 to 10 eggs in a clutch; the chicks are easy to rear. These birds eat pheasant pellets and must be wormed regularly.
Aviary size: Large.

The Copper Pheasant (Syrmaticus soemmerringi ijimae)
This pheasant comes from Japan where it is known as theYamdori. There are five sub-species but this is the one most commonly found in collections. The males and females can both be aggressive and will cross with the Reeves Pheasant. They start to breed in their first year and the hens lay 8 to 12 eggs in a clutch; the cock birds will need to be separated from the hens during the breeding season.
Aviary size: Medium to large.

47

RARE PHEASANTS WHICH ARE NOT AVAILABLE

Blyth's Tragopan (Tragopan blythi)

These birds are found in Bhutan and Tibet where they are heavily protected. This race is probably under the greatest pressure as the European genetic stock is weak despite successful A.I. breeding. Everyone is awaiting the arrival of new stock to improve the situation. The birds attain their full adult plumage in their second year when the hens start to lay, normally 2 to 4 eggs in a clutch.

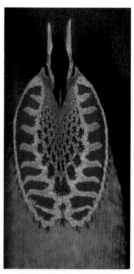

Front view of male displaying.

Western Tragopan (Tragopan melanocephalus)

This pheasant comes from the Eastern range of the Himalayas, Pakistan and North West India. At the moment there are no birds in Europe or the USA but there is a captive breeding progamme at the Saharan Pheasantry, Himachal Pradesh in India. The hens lay in their second year when they achieve their full adult plummage, probably 3 or 4 eggs in a clutch

The Crested Argus.

There are two sub-species of Crested Argus: Rheinart's Crested Argus (Rheinartia ocellata ocellata) which is found in the highlands of Vietnam and Laos, and the Malay Crested Argus (Rheinartia ocellata nigrescens) which is found in the hill forests of Malaysia; both are considered to be very rare, with only 10,000 individual birds still inhabiting Vietnam. The Crested Argus is distinguished by its huge tail feathers which are up to 5 inches wide and nearly 6 feet long in adult males. The female is darker and smaller with a shorter tail. They have been bred in America and France but are not known to be in captivity in the West now.

Head of Crested Argus in alarm mode.

Sclater's Monal (Lophophorus sclateri)
These birds live in the high mountainous areas of south east Tibet, Burma and south west China. Not a great deal is known about them in the wild although there are a few birds held in the Breeding Centre for Endangered Animals in Beijing, but none to be seen outside China.

Sara Roadnight

Chinese Monal (Lophophorus ihuysii) sometimes called the Chinese Impeyan.
These birds come from the high forested regions of central China. Again, there is little information about them in the wild although there are several kept in captivity at the San Diego Zoo, U.S.A.

51

BUYING PHEASANTS

When you are ready to buy your pheasants I would recommend that you go to an established breeder. Have a look at his aviaries and stock and if everything looks all right, buy your birds. (Ornamental pheasants are not normally sold as eggs or day old chicks unlike game pheasants.) Try to avoid dealers or auctions. One must remember that people often put birds into auctions to get rid of unwanted stock: the birds could easily be infertile or aggressive and although they might be cheaper at auction you could be buying a disease problem as well. Avoid cock pheasants with long spurs as they are likely to be old birds. Look for young birds if you can. You may have to wait a year or two before they are fully mature but it will be worth it; the pheasants will settle in and get to know you well as they are growing up.

The most important thing to remember when buying stock is to make sure your new birds are unrelated; in-breeding is a real problem with captive-bred birds and can eventually alter a species or even destroy it. The Blyth's Tragopan is a typical example of this. It also occurs in common species like the Golden Pheasant which has been crossed with the Lady Amherst's. The colouring usually gives the ancestry away: a Lady Amherst's Pheasant with a mainly red head and flecking on the body feathers is not a pure bird.

Birds in captivity live much longer than those in the wild as they are not subjected to predation from animals, other birds or humans, but in most cases it does not follow that they are fertile for a correspondingly longer time.

When buying endangered species check with the breeder which blood lines he keeps, and that you have the correct CITES paperwork to go with the birds.

AVIARIES

Aviary sizes are hotly debated within the pheasant keeping fraternity, and there are pheasant keepers who use pens smaller than those recommended here. It is all a matter of opinion but the larger the aviary the more it costs to build, although I believe it is better for the welfare and breeding potential of the birds.

Here are the main points to consider when setting out to construct an aviary or group of aviaries:

1) The aviary must be large enough for the birds and their welfare; they should be able to enjoy the sunshine in summer and winter, but be protected from the elements such as wind, rain and snow. Heated winter quarters are essential for some breeds. The aviary should also be large enough for the birds to settle and breed.

2) The aviary must be well drained, provide shelter, water and a covered area for feeding. It must meet the requirements of individual breeds and be secure against vermin and human intruders. It must also be secure against escapees because, under the current Wildlife and Countryside laws, you can be fined if you allow a non native bird to escape into the wild, unless you have a special license to do so.

3) The aviary should be planted with bushes, shrubs and climbers to enhance its appearance and provide cover for the birds. There needs to be enough room for maintenance to take place inside the pen without disturbing the birds unduly.

4) The aviary should give pleasure to the owner and visitors who should be able to see the birds without disturbing them.

5) Planning permission may be required before you put up your aviaries. It's also important to discuss your plans fully with your neighbours as they may be affected; pheasants do make a certain amount of noise from early in the morning and throughout the day.

Aviaries should be south facing to give the pheasants maximum sunlight. Never put an aviary under a tree in case of falling branches and to avoid a build-up of dead leaves on the roof. These can be a nuisance to get rid of, they restrict the light inside the aviary and put a strain on the structure.

Aviaries in the garden at Cleres, France.

Access is important not only for viewing the pheasants but also for maintenance, feeding, cleaning, egg collection etc. You can construct pathways from many different materials such as concrete, concrete slabs or paving stones, gravel, wood bark or chippings. There must be good drainage by the access paths to prevent puddles or soggy areas.

Electricity is necessary for lighting, heating, electric fencing and alarm systems. You will need lighting when you feed your birds on early winter mornings; you will also need it to lengthen the hours of daylight for those breeds that lay in the early Spring such as the Peacock Pheasants. Heating is essential for a number of non hardy breeds during cold weather. Water baths can be introduced into the aviaries on warm days but should not be left there all the time as they would collect leaves and other scratchings and would become a health hazard unless cleaned out daily. You will need a water supply for the birds, for washing drinkers or hands and for watering the plants in the aviary.

If you are not on free draining soil you will have to organise some drainage. This is important as there is nothing worse than flooded nests and pheasants paddling about in water, which could easily lead to an outbreak of coccidiosis. The aviaries will have to be raised to prevent them becoming waterlogged, and you need to plan how to take the water away from the covered areas and paths etc. Agricultural flexible drainage pipe is available in different sizes from 5cms to 20cms diameter. It is fairly cheap and once it has been laid and covered in pea-gravel it works well. Another way of achieving good drainage is to remove the top soil and back fill with 2" size clean aggregate then put down a layer of chipped bark which is kind on the birds' feet.

Runs may have to be covered in the event of an avian flu outbreak.

Designs

There are two different types of aviary, one for hardy breeds and the other for non-hardy breeds like Firebacks and some Peacock Pheasants. which require heating in the winter months.

Most people will want to build several aviaries, perhaps in a block or back to back, or in different groupings according to ground levels, locations and elevations. A plain square block would not look very attractive on its own so do your best to landscape it into the garden or planned area by adding rocks, shrubs, flower beds and pathways. You will need to build one or two extra aviaries to keep free so you have somewhere to put injured birds (particularly scalped ones) where they can recover; it's also useful if you are replanting an aviary or if you have a vicious cock bird that needs to be isolated from time to time.

It's important to plan your aviaries so they are interconnecting, not only from the shelter end but via the sides as well. This means that birds can be moved from pen to pen if necessary without being caught and stressed. With certain breeds, Reeves for example, there is a very aggresive streak in the cock birds which attack the hens during the breeding season. For this reason they should only spend a limited time each day with the hens so it is a big advantage if you can just shoo them into the next door pen or seperate cock pen with the minimum of stress.

Cock pens.

Size is often debated, but it's always best to give the birds as large an aviary as possible depending on the space available; nothing looks worse than long tailed pheasants in a small aviary with the cock bird's tail feathers broken off. In general the smallest pen for a pair or trio of birds should be no less than 4m by 4m (13ft x 13ft) which in total gives 16 sq m or 169 sq ft but Golden Pheasants and Lady Amherst Pheasants will tolerate smaller pens if necessary. Medium sized pens should be about 24 sq m or 245 sq ft and large sized pens should be over 35 sq m or 370 sq ft, suitable for the Koklass Pheasant for example.

Both heated and non-heated aviaries can come in three kinds: utilitarian, breeding or exhibition. The first are used as holding aviaries for young maturing birds and the second are normally quieter places where the birds have a chance to breed without being disturbed; the third tend to be more expensively planted although not too densely so the birds can still be seen. When planting an aviary it can be difficult to achieve the correct balance between too little or too much cover for the pheasants, as you don't want to create a 'spot the pheasant' situation! Thus exhibition aviaries tend to be more square in shape and not too deep whereas breeding and utilitarian aviaries are more oblong.

When designing your aviaries don't forget to incorporate a plan of the shelter at the rear and the planting you wish to do. The front of the aviary should be fairly open with low growing shrubs to allow the sunshine in and provide an area where the cock bird can display. If you offer your birds titbits in this area they will get used to showing themselves to people. Further back plant taller vegetation such as grasses or bamboo where the birds can conceal themselves and make nests. It's important to allow for plenty of room inside the pens so that you can get in to prune shrubs, collect eggs and rake the

A simple aviary design.

narrow walkways used by the pheasants. The pens should not be cluttered with vegetation and there must be sufficient visibility to be able to check your birds' welfare. The shelter area at the rear should have a sand floor; it is used by the pheasants for feeding and drinking and is where they roost at night.

Last but not least, it's very important to make the whole area vermin proof, not only against foxes, owls and hawks but also two legged predators!

A simple beginner's aviary.

Plan view

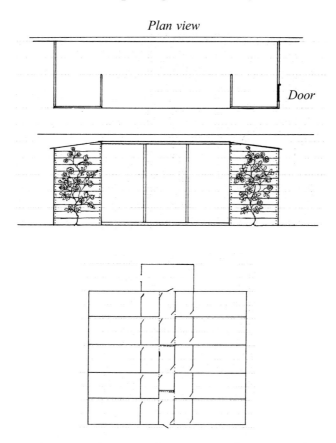

Door

A block of breeding or stock aviaries showing access from a central corridor. Along the corridor are two mobile wire frames which are used for moving birds from one aviary to another without catching them. Alternatively, if you need to catch birds it's easier to do so in the corridor rather than among the plants in the aviary.

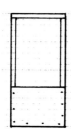

Mobile frames.
Plyboard up to 4ft and wire mesh above.
These frames are held in place by metal pins.

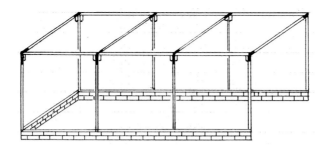

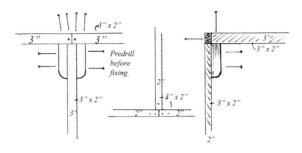

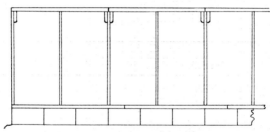

This is a strong construction using 3" x 2"
sitting on and fixed to breeze blocks.

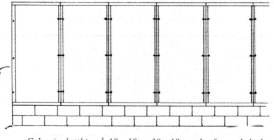

Use 3" x 3" on the
corner frames.
This marries up
better with
adjoining frames
and gives added
strength.

Galvanised weldmesh 1" x 1" on 3" x 1" wooden frames bolted
together and fixed to 2 layers of house bricks.

Construction and materials

When you make an aviary your aim is to make sure that no predators can get in and no pheasants can get out. It is essential to use wire netting or mesh (although plastic netting is now becoming popular) and this is fixed onto a wooden or metal framework. The advantage of using wire mesh is that you can achieve wider panels without any sag in the material. The same can't be said for netting which has to be put under tension to prevent it from bulging; this means that you will have to use stronger posts to cope with the strain. Wire mesh is more expensive than plastic netting.

A covered rat trap.

It is best to use a 1" wire mesh from the ground up, and then a light 1.5" or 2" mesh above it; join the two meshes together with wire clips. Some people prefer to use 1" mesh all the way up to keep out wild birds like sparrows and so cut down on the introduction of worms and diseases; conversely, others like to use the 2" mesh because they find that chaffinches and other small birds nest in the bushes in the aviary where they are safe from hawks and other predators. However, it's important to be aware that rats, mink and stoats can climb very well so you must be extremely vigilant with your trapping. Place tunnel traps strategically round the outside of your aviaries, preferably out of sight of visitors, and don't forget to check them daily. For detailed information on predators and trapping see the book 'Modern Vermin Control' in the Gold Cockerel Series. The major threats to pheasants in aviaries are foxes, badgers, dogs, cats, rats, mink, squirrels, owls and hawks, and to a lesser extent mice

Plan view of the inside of a covered area showing access doors, popholes and perches. This plan is designed for excluding the male during breeding times.

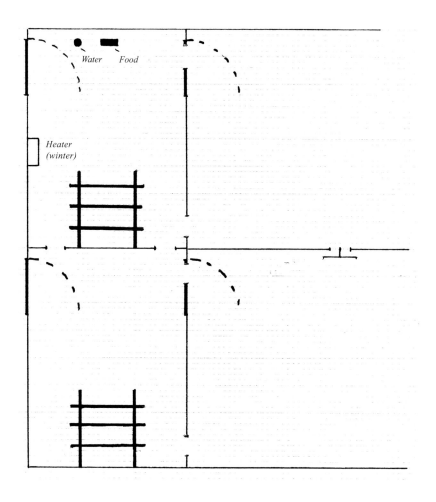

Water   Food

Heater
(winter)

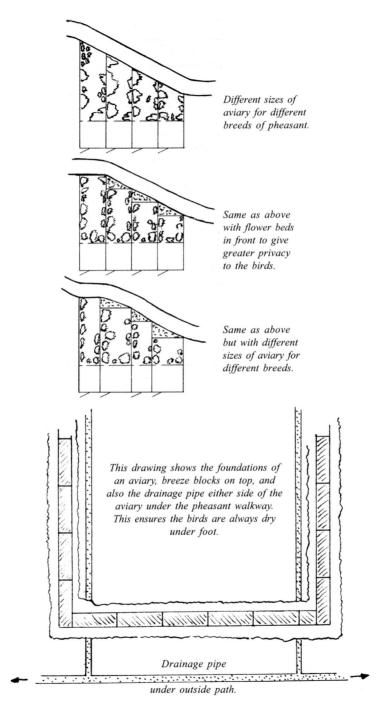

*Different sizes of
aviary for different
breeds of pheasant.*

*Same as above
with flower beds
in front to give
greater privacy
to the birds.*

*Same as above
but with different
sizes of aviary for
different breeds.*

*This drawing shows the foundations of
an aviary, breeze blocks on top, and
also the drainage pipe either side of the
aviary under the pheasant walkway.
This ensures the birds are always dry
under foot.*

Drainage pipe

under outside path.

and wild birds like sparrows.

An aviary must be 7ft or 8ft high; any lower and it will be difficult to walk in. It is also important to give the birds a feeling of space and height in their environment.

An easy way to make the aviary is to construct frames and then bolt them together. The frames can be put together indoors on jigs before the mesh or netting is stapled to them. These panels are normally 6ft high and 4ft wide with 1ft long legs onto which skirting boards are attached. These boards are not always used but do prevent draughts and give the pheasants more privacy; they also stop young chicks from escaping if the birds are rearing their own. The boards can vary in height from 12" to 30" depending on the breed of pheasant.

If you have well drained soil you may be able to construct your aviary without a raised floor. This means that your wire mesh will have to be sunk into the ground for at least 15cms all the way round with a further 30cms laid out flat at right angles to stop foxes from digging their way in. Aviaries are usually best raised off the ground by about 1ft, so you will have to dig trenches to a depth of 1ft to 18" for the foundations. At this stage plastic drainage pipes need to be laid along the insides of the pen and under where the walkways are going to be, then joined up with the main drainage system.

Once the trenches have been dug they are filled with concrete and levelled; you may have to step them if the ground is sloping. Your posts will need to be concreted in at this stage, and don't forget, wooden posts must always be made of treated wood.

When your posts are in you can start building a low wall on top of the foundations using concrete blocks, bricks or stone; this wall can be 6", 9" or 12" high. Put down some pea gravel round the drainage pipe then fill the whole area with soil, using a dumper truck if you can to save time. Create a few hillocks if you wish and add sand for the pathways; (try to incorporate curves and dog legs in the paths to discourage your birds from pacing), then you can bring the aviary sections and cross members for the posts ready for assembling.

Now you are ready to start laying the turf and putting in your plants.

When this is all complete you can then put up the sections and fix the cross members. For the roof you can use 1.5" mesh polythene game bird netting. This will stop a pheasant damaging itself if it gets spooked and flies up and knocks its head on the roof. The mesh is also the right size to prevent a bird from hanging itself. One disadvantage is that squirrels can eat their way through the mesh so it needs to be checked weekly; to overcome this some people have two roofs on their aviaries, wire mesh above and polythene netting below it to prevent head damage. It's important to remember that heavy snow can be a problem in winter, so make sure that the top cross members of the aviary are strong enough to take the weight. Failing that, temporary props can be put in place during snowy weather.

The shelter area should be constructed out of corrugated tin sheeting and 8ft by 4ft sheets of three eighths of an inch or half inch exterior grade plyboard. Half of the tin sheeting should be sunk into the ground and the plyboard and wooden framework should be fixed to the top; this

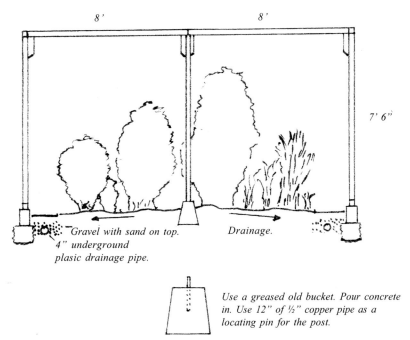

8'   8'

7' 6"

Gravel with sand on top.   Drainage.
4" underground
plasic drainage pipe.

Use a greased old bucket. Pour concrete in. Use 12" of ½" copper pipe as a locating pin for the post.

prevents rats from gnawing their way through at ground level. For the roof use galvanised box section sheets which come in a range of lengths; for light use box section fibreglass sheets. These are fairly expensive but last longer than plastic ones. Do NOT use roof felt as it harbours red mite which can lower a bird's resistance to disease by sucking its blood at night. Thought should be given to getting water away from the roof via gutters and down pipes.

Inside the sheltered area there is a floor of sand, a ladder roost or perches, feed hopper and drinker. The food can be kept dry here and out of the sight of sparrows, and the food hopper and drinker can be serviced daily from the back door. The droppings under the perch should be cleared up and fresh sand put down if necessary.

Some pheasants prefer to roost outside in the run and provision must be made for this. Perches must be quite high, about 5ft, and a minimum of 3" (7.5cms) in diameter so the birds have a wide edge to rest their breasts on: they don't stand up all night but clutch the perch and settle down covering their feet with their breast feathers, which prevents frost bite in cold climates. You can provide electric lighting in the covered area or thermostatically controlled heaters if necessary; blow heaters are the best.

The floor in the aviary is all important. Apart from the planted areas the floors should either be grass, coarse sand or bark. Grass can be strimmed or cut by hand and there is a special plastic netting available which sinks down into the turf and protects it from diggers or scratchers like Eared or Monal Pheasants. You will have to cover the roots of any plants in the aviary with this netting to protect them as well Sand or

A range of aviaries constructed in polytunnels.

bark must be raked regularly to keep it clean and healthy.

If you want a larger aviary you could use a polytunnel. These work extremely well, giving the birds a feeling of space and light, and as the tunnels are modular you can make the aviary as long as you like. The metal hoops support the netting down to about a metre from the ground and heavy duty plastic netting is attached all round the bottom. It is vital to have good fox fencing and electric fences if you are using this system, and watch out when there are heavy falls of snow!

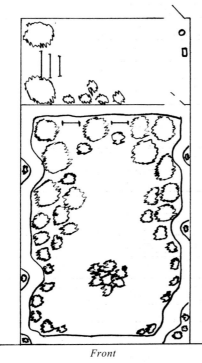

Sheltered and heated area with vegetation, perches, drinker and feeder.

Note pophole in the door. Sand.

Walkway of coarse sand with interruptions along the length.

Roosting areas.

Display and sunbathing areas.

Nesting areas.

Grass.

Front

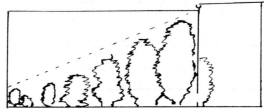

The taller plants should be at the back of the aviary. This gives maximum sunlight and visibility.

Front.

PLANTING

Aviaries without plants are like houses without furniture; the choice of plants is obviously up to the individual and will vary according to location and soils.

It can be difficult to decide what to plant as there is so much available, but evergreens are good for year round cover and there is a list of flowering evergreens below. The advantage of most evergreen shrubs is that you can prune them hard if necessary and they always grow back well, but this is more difficult with conifers.

Never plant trees; remember, too much shade will kill the grass in an aviary, and grass is important for Koklass and Eared-Pheasants particularly. Shrub habit varies considerably from bush and climbing to horizontal and vertical; it is important to be aware of this when siting a plant. Avoid vigorous species such as leyandii, or prickly ones like holly, pyracantha or gorse: remember you have to go into the aviary regularly to rake the pathways, clear debris and prune plants so you don't want anything that will overwhelm the space or be prickly or scratchy to handle. Other plants to avoid are poisonous ones like yew or laburnum (which are trees anyway) and rampant climbers like Russian Vine, ivy or Virginia Creeper and some climbing roses. Plants in the Juniper family are excellent for providing slow growing ground cover, and grape vines and currants are ideal for aviaries as they provide food for the pheasants as well as looking decorative. Passion Flowers, Buddleia and Hypericum also add colour and cover.

Arbutus	Cotoneaster	Lavandula	Pittosporum
Aucuba	Daphne	Lonicera	Rhododendron
Camellia	Erica	Mahonia	Skimmia
Choisya	Hebe	Myrtus	Viburnam
Clematis	Jasminum	Osmanthus	

Small bamboos, Juncus reed and certain grasses including pampas grass, are useful additions to an aviary.

Apart from plants, aviaries also need a variety of tree boughs, logs, stumps and large rocks. These furnishings play an important part in courtship displays and provide the pheasants with opportunities for more activity, like a kind of playground. This helps to stop them becoming bored which means they are less stressed and calmer. You can always add more leylandii, pine or fir branches at nesting time.

A well planted aviary. Note the tree stump and log 'furnishings'.

SECURITY AND ALARMS

There are often unscrupulous people about who prefer to steal birds or their eggs rather than pay for them, and there is nothing worse than going to feed your birds in the morning and finding them gone.

It's all very well to have padlocks on your aviary doors but a determined thief will unscrew the hinges and get in that way; if you fit the doors with the hinges on the inside there should not be a problem.

Lights with a sensor that come on after dark are a good deterrent, and there are several types of security alarm available which can link up to your house or telephone. They work in various ways, for example, a cicuit is broken when a door is opened, or there are pads concealed under a section of floor, or there are electric beams which an intruder would break if he walked through them. There are also CCTV cameras of course. You should shop around for a system that suits you; the Internet is always a good place to start.

Remember that there are small animals like mice or bats about 24 hours a day, so

Electric fencing.

your alarms should not be too sensitive. It's also a good idea to have two systems working to be absolutely sure that it is an intruder that has set them off.

GENERAL MANAGEMENT

Good general management combines feeding, watering, worming and cleaning with gardening, recording and last but not least, observing. It is a matter of organising a strict routine and sticking to it while using observation continually. Take time to watch your birds whenever you can so that you can spot any changes as soon as they occur. It's a good idea to whistle to them as you get near the aviary; this warns them of your approach, makes them less nervous and helps to build up a rapport with them. Keep an eye on the droppings as they are a good indiction of health (they should be brown with a white tip), and listen to your birds breathing: can you hear any gasping or "snicking", or is there any discharge coming from nostrils or eyes? Most of these symptoms are covered in the section on Diseases. It's helpful if the birds are used to coming for titbits of raisins or nuts as it draws them closer to you and you can observe them more easily.

You will have to organise a worming programme. Use Flubendazole (trade name Flubenvet) once or twice a year; it is a very safe drug and kills all the worms present, not just a few of them. It is a fine white powder and is best added to feed pellets or wheat with a little olive oil to make it stick; without this it would trickle down and accumulate in the bottom of the food hopper. Although your pheasants will not be roaming free range in the open they are still at risk from worms as small wild birds like sparrows will be perching on top of the aviary and regularly leaving droppings inside. We have had cock birds that would start to show signs of distress although still attentive to their hens, and they have suddenly keeled over and died, riddled with worms and light as a feather.

Management includes a maintenance programme, that is pruning bushes, cutting grass, raking pathways, removing droppings from under perches, checking for red mite and washing drinkers. The buildings will also need painting regularly and the gutters will need cleaning out.

Records are important along with leg ringing or wing tagging. You will be able to keep details of the age of your birds, when they were hatched or bought and the blood line, as well as anything else you might need to record such as first egg, fertility, etc and of course any treatments for diseases. See section on Identification and Recording.

If you are introducing new birds to your existing ones it's a good idea to put them all into a fresh aviary together; that way your established birds will be too busy checking out their new accomodation to bother with bullying the newcomers.

FEEDING

In general most ornamental pheasants live on a diet of wheat and pheasant pellets together with supplements.

Pheasant pellets are made specially for pheasants and there are four main types: there is a starter crumb for day old chicks and young growers, a rearing pellet for growers, a breeding pellet for use before and during the breeding season and a maintenance pellet which is used out of the breeding season. Each of these foods contains a different level of protein and vitamins. You can also add cut maize to these rations but use it sparingly as it is rather fattening. When buying a bag of pellets it is important to check the sell-by date to make sure the food will still be fresh by the time you finish it.

A selection of fruit and vegetables suitable for pheasants.

You can feed your pheasants either in a hopper, (pigeon hoppers work well) which could last them a week or more, or in a covered container which you fill daily. The choice is up to you and depends on your life style, but the latter method is really better as you can keep a check on the food consumption per pen. If you are adding new birds to an established aviary of pheasants, don't forget to put in more drinkers and feeders so that the newcomers are not pushed away from the food. You can also offer your birds titbits such as peanuts, raisons or grapes each day, and they will get used to coming to you. Like this it is easy to spot if one of them is off colour and not interested in its food, in which case it should be caught, weighed and checked over.

There are three groups of pheasants that require a more vegetarian diet, Blood Pheasants, Koklass and Tragopans; these will want a daily ration of chopped lettuce, carrot, apple and banana as well as their usual pellets, and all types of pheasant will enjoy a weekly supplement of Red Band which is a mixture of seeds and nuts. Apart from these standard rations you should vary your birds' diet as much as possible to keep them interested in life and in tip-top condition; but remember, too much of a particular food such as peanuts can be bad for them, either because it is fattening or upsets the digestion. So offer a good variety of foods and take note of what they like; cold or warm baked or boiled potatoes are always a good standby. Never leave food, particularly fruit, out for more than 24 hours to add more next time, and don't leave it lying in the sun. The fruit and vegetables that you will be using are apples, bananas, pears, plums, currants and grapes, beetroot, carrots, swede, peas and lettuce (green leafy type chopped). You can also sprinkle the chopped food with hempseed, linseed, black sunflower seeds and a few raisons or sultanans. It would be very helpful to get on friendly terms with your local greengrocer!

A secure food store.

When you have new birds always try in the beginning to incorporate some of the pheasant pellets they have been used to, if different from your own. They will probably need encouraging to feed because of the new

73

surroundings and noises, so offer them a good variety of food such as cold baked potatoes, raw or cooked carrot, grapes, raspberries, cat food, any of the fruits or vegetables listed above, as well as your own brand of pheasant pellets of course. This is also a good time to worm them with Flubenvet (see chapter on Diseases and Ailments).

Occasionally, if you have a sick bird you can offer a meat feed. Try maggots, mealworms or crickets or failing that some fishy cat food.

Grit is very important. Depending on the size of your birds you can use either mixed poultry grit or wild bird grit which is much finer. There are three types of grit all of which are important: oyster shell or sea shell is absorbed into the bird's system to help form strong egg shells, limestone is for bones and flint goes into the gizzard to grind down seeds such as wheat, cut maize, or hemp etc. Grit is best given to the birds in a cage cup, a plastic container with two hooks on the side which hook onto the wire netting; drill a few holes in the bottom to allow any water to drain out.

There are all kinds of vitamin supplements on the market that you can add either to the pheasants' food or drinking water. These are certainly worth trying, although some are very expensive, so find out what other breeders use and listen to their comments.

Fresh drinking water is essential for your birds. I once met a Dutch breeder who never gave his pheasants water from the tap but only the bottled kind!

BREEDING

This is the time when you have to be observant without being intrusive. Try to ensure that the birds in the aviary are the same age and as young as possible. Ornamental pheasants are usually kept in pairs, occasionally trios (two females and one male) because if there is more than one male in an aviary they will fight over the female(s), particularly during the breeding season. It's important to avoid in-breeding, and you should also bear in mind that certain breeds such as the Eared-Pheasants, the Swinhoe, Silver, Golden and Lady Amherst's amongst others, will only lay and be fertile in their second year. If you can introduce the birds to each other well before Christmas they will be nicely settled together by the following February.

Two types of shelter for hens.

Worm your pheasants with Flubenvet and then step up the protein from the winter ration pellet to a breeder pellet. At this stage introduce some more cover into the aviary in the form of pine or fir branches and put down some sand and loose hay. Leylandii branches are excellent for creating cover and sheltered nesting places as they hold their foliage well. This is important, particularly for some breeds such as the Reeves, the Copper and the Hume's Pheasant for example, whose males become aggressive in the breeding season and the hens need to hide away. You can make simple shelters for the hens out of plastic barrels cut in half and a hole cut out of one end, or an inverted V made from two boards about 30" long joined together; the height of the boards depends on the size of the birds. Some breeds such as Tragopans require nesting boxes or baskets raised off the ground; these can be situated among clumps of bamboo or other coarse grasses. Even if a pair of birds have been together for years the cock can turn on the hen and attack her for no apparent reason. We had experience of this when our first pair of Cabot's Tragopan, which had been together for three years with never a cross word, suddenly came to blows: one spring morning we found the hen hiding in a bush almost completely scalped. Luckily she survived, having been expertly sewn up by the vet, but that ended any hopes of fertile eggs that Spring - a whole year wasted!

A nesting basket.

You may find you have to put up some temporary higher dividing walls to give your pheasants more privacy; some people have to isolate certain birds which are put off by the calling of neighbouring birds of the same breed. The Lewis's Silver Pheasant (Lophura nycthemera lewisi) has been found to breed best in an aviary that has black polythene sheeting from the floor to the roof; this makes going into the aviary rather a surreal experience as the only light comes through the roof, but if the space is well planted the birds seem to settle and breed well.

You will always find that young birds lay a week or two later than older ones of the same breed; in northern latitudes it will be necessary to organise extra lighting to help the breeding process along. Some hens need a little encouragement to start nesting so you could provide a box approximately 40 x 40 x 20cms high with a little soil and some straw in the bottom.

You will need to provide extra oyster shell grit so the hen pheasants can make good strong egg shells but you may find that you have a problem with egg eating which is the bane of all bird keepers' lives and difficult to stop! Sometimes it is the cock bird who is the culprit, in which case he must be separated from the hen, being put in to mate with her after she has laid and then removed. See section on Egg Eating.

Eggs should be collected once a day and twice on warm days; don't touch the hen's first egg, just record the date that it was laid. Try to enter the pen when the she is off the nest so that you disturb her as little as possible. Mark each egg with the breed and the date using an HB pencil.

Screened aviary for Lewis's Silver Pheasants.

EGGS

When you collect your pheasant eggs don't forget to write on each one the initials of the breed that laid it. You may find that some are dirty. I don't agree with washing eggs myself, but always remove any dirt or faeces by scraping it off with a knife or rubbing it gently with wire wool. If you do wish to wash your eggs, use a proprietary egg washing fluid such as Deosan, but remember that using chemicals on hatching eggs can reduce their hatchability.

Egg hygiene.

The eggs need to be turned each day. Store them in a cool brick or stone shed or cellar on a bed of sand 3" deep (8cms) inside a shallow box or on clean kitchen paper. Lay them on their sides so that the writing is either visible or not visible on all of them; like this you can see which eggs have been turned and which have not. The eggs must be kept cool because if they get too warm, 70 degrees or more, they will start to germinate. This can happen when the weather gets warmer or in hot countries so use an air cooling unit in hot weather or climates.

If you have several different breeds of pheasant then you will have to make some careful calculations to ensure that all your eggs hatch on the same day. Incubation times vary between breeds, for example, a Golden Pheasant egg takes 22 days to hatch whereas a Hume's Bar-tailed Pheasant egg takes 28 days. This also applies if you are using a broody hen as the different eggs will need to be put under her on different days.

Remember, for optimum hatching try to avoid keeping eggs for more than 7 days in storage; you can stretch it to 10 days in cool weather but it's best not to.

Egg Eating

This can be a problem and is nearly always started by the cock bird. A persistent egg eater can never be cured and will have to be got rid of but there are a few things you can do to try and stop it. It occurs only with certain pairs of birds and it doesn't seem to be connected with particular breeds. Good nesting cover is essential; you can try putting golf or ping pong balls into the nest boxes or nesting areas early in the year as this sometimes thwarts the egg eaters, but it doesn't always work. Another option is to put game bird 'bits' on your pheasants; bits are small C shaped pieces of plastic which fit into the nostrils and seperate the top and bottom parts of the beak preventing it from closing completely; the bird can still eat, drink and breathe properly. This may not be a practical solution and if it is the cock bird that is the culprit, then you must ensure that he is out of the pen when the hen is about to lay. This means that he will be put in with the hen on alternate days as they normally lay every other day.

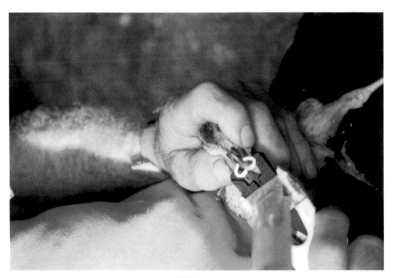

Bitting.

79

INCUBATION

The main advantage of incubators over broodies is that machines are available at any time of year and don't need feeding while they are not incubating.

If you are thinking about buying an incubator it is best to have it installed well before you need to use it. It's also a very good idea to have a separate hatcher, as hatching is the dirty part of the whole operation with a lot of bacteria flying around; in fact it would be ideal if you could arrange to hatch in a separate room altogether.

Siting the incubator is all important: you need a room with a constant ambient temperature, not too hot or too cold. A north facing spare room would be ideal or a room in a stone or brick building with a slate or tiled floor.

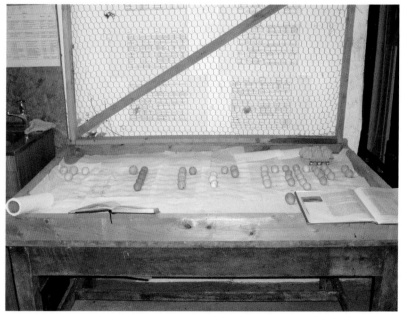

Storing eggs prior to incubation.

You will obviously be aware that many of the eggs you are going to incubate are from rare and very valuable birds so it's vital that you have an incubator that is reliable and works well; try to buy a slightly larger model than you require. Small incubators range in price from about £100-00 to £900-00 so the sale of three or four pairs of pheasants would go a long way towards paying for one.

It is possible to find second-hand incubators for sale at the end of the season. If you can find one that is not too old it could be a good buy but you would have to thoroughly clean and sterilise it before use. When you buy any incubator, new or second-hand, always have a trial run with some hen or bantam eggs first to get used to the machine. Keep a record of everything you do to refer to in the future. It is imperative to follow the manufacturer's instructions exactly as incubation is a complex and delicate operation, a complete science in its own right. No two people are likely to achieve the same results even if they use the same equipment.

Use Virkon S to thoroughly clean and sterilise the incubator between hatches. A lot of manufacturers neglect to say how important this is. More poor hatches are caused by bacteria left over from the previous batch of eggs than by anything else.

For further information on incubation read 'Incubation at Home' from the Gold Cockerel Series of books.

INCUBATION TIMES

18 - 19 DAYS   Palawan Peacock Pheasant

21 - 22 DAYS   Germain's Peacock Pheasant
                        Grey Peacock Pheasant

22 DAYS   Bronze-tailed Peacock Pheasant
                        Edward's Pheasant
                        Vietnamese Pheasant
                        Malaysian Peacock Pheasant

22 - 23 DAYS   Golden Pheasant
                        Lady Amherst's Pheasant

23 DAYS   Rothschild's Peacock Pheasant

23 - 24 DAYS   Malaysian Crestless Fireback
                        Vieillot's Crested Fireback

24 DAYS   Bornean Crested Fireback

24 - 25 DAYS   Crested Argus
                        Great Argus
                        Kalij
                        Siamese Fireback
                        True Pheasant
                        White Eared-Pheasant

24 - 26 DAYS	Bulwer's Wattled Pheasant
25 DAYS	Copper Pheasant
	Elliot's Pheasant
	Reeves Pheasant
	Salvadori's Pheasant
	Silver Pheasant
	Swinhoe's Pheasant
26 DAYS	Brown Eared-Pheasant
	Cheer Pheasant
26 - 27 DAYS	Blue Eared-Pheasant
	Koklass Pheasant
27 DAYS	Mikado Pheasant
27 - 29 DAYS	Blood Pheasant
28 DAYS	Cabot's Tragopan
	Hume's Bar-Tailed Pheasant
	Monal
	Temminck's Tragopan
	Western Tragopan
28 - 30 DAYS	Blyth's Tragopan
	Satyr Tragopan

These figures are all subject to altitude and temperature variations.

CANDLING

Candling is a method of checking the development of the chick inside the egg. It is called 'candling' because originally candles were used to shine light through the egg in a dark room.

Early electric candlers had a bulb in a wooden box with a hole for the beam of light. Today we have progressed to hand-held electric candlers which you place against the 'blunt' end of the egg. The advantage of these is that you do not have to touch the egg which cuts down on the possible transmission of bacteria. It is more difficult to see into dark shelled eggs, but candling in subdued light with a bright bulb helps. High efficiency bulbs, halogen for example, produce more light without a proportionately high heat output. To prevent the heat harming the embryo don't hold the candler against the egg for any length of time - you only need a few seconds.

When candling you must avoid unplugging the incubator heater; if you do not have separate sockets for the heater, turner and candler, use the turning mechanism socket.

Day ten is the first candling day. The embryo looks like a large red spider with a red blob in the middle; this is the heart and you should be able to see it beating. There is a clearly defined air sac and the egg should be dark and cloudy. A clear egg has a poorly defined air sac and lights up when the torch shines through it. When you candle it on its side the yolk floats around and always comes to the top of the egg. If you are unsure of the development leave it another week or compare it with a fertile egg of the same species at the same stage. Remove any clears.

Day sixteen is the next candling period. Take out any eggs that have not progressed.

On day twenty-two check again on the chick's development inside the egg. When you candle near to hatching time you will see the chick move its head away from the light.

BROODIES

The question of which breed of bantam or hen to choose is often hotly debated and every broody user has his or her favourite. Most people use a Silkie, normally crossed with a clean legged bantam like a Light Sussex. There are two reasons for this: first, the Silkie's leg feathers can be very sharp and harmful to small pheasant chicks, and secondly, pure Silkies can be prone to Scaley Leg disease. This does not mean that Silkies should not be used, quite the contrary, but you should be aware of these shortcomings. Some people use Old English Game bantams, the choice is wide and individual; the most important thing is that the broody does her job and can often be coaxed into sitting for several months providing the eggs are removed several days before hatching; if she hears the chicks peeping, she will come out of broody mode and stop sitting.

At the end of January before the season starts, worm your broodies with Flubenvet and check them for Scaley Leg, then check them for Mycoplasma by sniffing their nostrils; if any of them smell vile or make a 'snicking' noise discard them. It's important to have Mycoplasma free stock if you possibly can. Hens, bantams and pheasants share many common diseases and ailments so it is essential these are not passed on to the pheasant chicks. Next your broodies need to be de-loused and de-fleaed. Sit down with a hen on some newspaper on your lap. Turn her

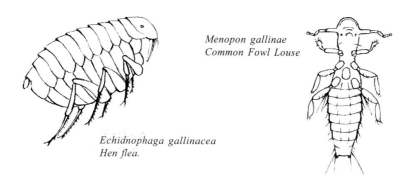

Menopon gallinae
Common Fowl Louse

Echidnophaga gallinacea
Hen flea.

Silkie cockerels with Pekin hens.

Silkie cockerel with Light Sussex bantam hens.

Light Sussex cockerel with Silkie hens.

Pens of birds for producing ideal broody hens.

over and sprinkle flea/louse powder onto her breast; work the powder round the neck, under the wings and round the vent area and the tail. Then turn the bird over again and dust her along the back and neck right up to the head. It's very important to do this as the main reason for broodies 'standing up' and leaving their eggs is a high flea or louse burden.

Next you need to encourage the hens to go broody and this is done by putting clusters of 3 or 4 crock eggs in each nest box which should do the trick. Remove any newly laid eggs.

A Silkie cross broody will sit on 6 to 10 pheasant eggs depending on the size of the eggs.

The traditional way of setting broodies gives the best results. You will need some broody boxes to begin with and these are constructed with wire netting on the base to prevent rats burrowing in. The boxes are set directly onto the earth which allows beneficial natural moisture to come up through the nest. The boxes can be made in rows of any number, but four or five are convenient and easy to handle before and after the hatching season. They should be set on a small mound about two turves high in case there

Silkie cross broodies.

is a lot of rain, and in the shade; they must not get too hot as this is likely to put the broody off. Punch a shallow dip like a saucer in a turf which is grass-side down and lay it in a box. Line the depression thinly with sweet hay or straw and make sure the turf fits snuggly inside with no room for the eggs to get rolled out into the cold. Make a nest like this in each box then put crock eggs or marked fresh eggs into each nest ready for the broodies; they need to sit steady on these for a few days before you put in the eggs you want them to hatch.

Broodies will not want to leave the nest if they are serious, and will guard any eggs jealously, fluffing up their feathers and grumbling at you, even pecking at intruding hands. In order to check that your selected broody is serious, take out any eggs from under her and slide your hand in palm up; she should "cuddle" your hand with her wings. If your broodies are not used to being handled it is best to put them into a cardboard box with straw and eggs and close the lid. You will then be able to transport them to

Rearing ark with improvised shelter.

the broody boxes easily. Let the hens sit quietly inside their cardboard box for an hour or two to regain their composure, then you can pop them gently into the broody boxes onto the crock eggs already there. Probably the best way is to move them when it is nearly dark.

It is advisable to get your broodies off the nest every day. Try to do this always at the same time, and tether them far enough apart so that they cannot fight. To tether, use a thong or piece of string attached to the broody's leg with a sliding loop and on the other end a curtain ring dropped over a three foot high stick. Water and whole wheat only must be within reach and the birds should be off the nest for about 20 minutes. Check that each hen has defecated before you gently put her back; if she has not you may have to help the process by raising her to waist height and then dropping her on the ground; several times may be necessary. As you are putting her back on the nest check that her feet are clean - hen manure will quickly turn the eggs bad. If you want to use a system of putting the birds in individual wire cages when taken off the nest, it is an alternative to tethering but involves more equipment.

When the broodies have sat on the crock eggs for a few days and become accustomed to whatever method you use for getting them off the nest, it is time to set the eggs you want hatched.

Put the eggs under the broodies in the evening, not forgetting to take away the crock eggs first. After about an hour check that all the eggs are covered and take away any that are not. An odd number of eggs fits into a circle.

Broody with chicks.

A good broody stays broody until she hatches off some chicks. This may be after 21 days or three months if you are juggling the eggs around to make the best use of the hens. Don't be afraid to keep a broody sitting on crock eggs until you are ready to set some eggs for hatching. When you do this try to set two or three clutches at the same time; this means that, having discarded infertile or bad ones, you will be able to amalgamate the remaining eggs under one of the broodies. If one of the birds does become fierce and insists on pecking you she is only trying to protect her eggs. Offer your hand palm uppermost where the thicker skin will withstand the pecks better, and turn your hand over once it is under the bird. Long sleeves are useful but protective gloves are not really recommended as you can't feel what you are doing.

Finally, there are some people who like to use both broodies and an incubator, the broodies for sitting on the eggs and the incubator for hatching them. This system has its advantages, particularly with small and often rare breeds of pheasant where there is a chance that the chicks might be trampled by the broody.

Don't forget to candle your eggs during brooding. This should be done at 10 days, 16 days and 22 days depending on the breed. Any infertiles can be removed, and where possible, clutches amalgamated. See section on Candling.

When hatching day arrives do not remove the broody or the chicks will chill as they struggle out of their shells. The broody can go 30 hours without food or water in these circumstances. Try not to disturb her too much during this period but do remove any larger pieces of empty shell just in case a smaller hatching egg gets lodged inside one.

Once all the chicks have hatched, or all that look as though they are going to make it, move the broody and young to a broody coop.

REARING

There are three different methods of rearing:
A) Parent rearing
B) Rearing under a broody bantam
C) Rearing under a heat lamp or electric hen

A) Parent rearing

If you are not concerned with obtaining the maximum number of eggs from a particular pair of pheasants you can adopt this system with certain species. We have had experience of a pair of Siamese Firebacks who consistently laid two clutches and then sat on the third, rearing them with great success. The hen must not have any kind of disturbance while she is sitting, and you should have an incubator on stand by just in case she leaves the nest. There is always a danger that the cock bird may kill the chicks, also your vermin control must be red hot as rats, weasels or mink will take the young birds, and there is the possibility of them escaping through the wire mesh. In spite of all this I personally find it a very satisfying method of breeding if it can be achieved.

B) Rearing under a broody

This is the traditional method but it has its drawbacks as do all the systems. It can be more time consuming, the youngsters occasionally get caught up in the broody's leg feathers and can become subject to hens' diseases. The hen sometimes squashes the chicks, so avoid breeds that have very small offspring if you are using this method. The advantages are that the poults feather up better and more quickly, and pheasants reared under hens are quieter and rarely have a problem with feather pecking.

Place the broody coop on level well mown grass or lawn. If the ground is not level you will find chicks escaping from the broody coop through the dips and holes round the edge unless you have wire mesh on the bottom. Leave the broody sitting until all the eggs that are going to have hatched, then move her and the chicks into the broody coop and add additional day old chicks to the brood if necessary; be careful when you do this and only put in chicks of approximately the same size and colour otherwise they may be rejected. Also, White Eared and Reeves chicks can be very vicious and attack newcomers.

Siamese Fireback poults with broody.

The broody coop should have a solid floor in the shelter end and 0.5" wire mesh under the run to prevent vermin getting in and chicks getting out.

Provide the broody with a water font and some pheasant starter crumbs mixed with a small handful of whole wheat in a chick feeder. One of the first things she will do as she settles in is produce a rather large smelly mess, so remove this as soon as you can. There is no need to put down any bedding like shavings or straw as the broody would only scatter it about and it would get into the food and water.

Move the broody coop regularly after the first 4 days, clean it out when necessary and give the chicks and hen fresh water and food daily. After 3 weeks move the chicks onto rearer pellets and watch the feathers grow! You will notice the young poults becoming more independant of the broody; by 5 to 8 weeks, depending on breed, they can be moved to the rearing pens.

C) Rearing under a lamp or electric hen

The advantages of this system are that you can have a row of rearing boxes which are convenient to manage and keep free of disease; it is also an easy way to rear batches of chicks of the same age, size and breed. (Take care when adding chicks to a batch: White Eared and Reeves pheasant chicks can be very vicious towards newcomers and attack and kill them.) The disadvantages are that it is more expensive with higher set up costs, and there can be more problems with feather pecking.

Most pheasant breeders rear under lamps and a few use electric hens. Lamps should be ceramic bulbs not white or red ones. This is because ceramic bulbs produce heat without light which means the chicks can sleep in the darkness at night: chicks grow in their sleep. Never suspend your ceramic bulb by the flex only but use a light chain so you can adjust the height of the bulb above the ground or floor of the rearing box. If there is no natural light available you will have to provide some electric lighting with a dimmer switch for the end of the day: it is important that the light dims gradually because if it were to switch off suddenly the chicks could be caught in the dark away from the heat source.

If your birds are housed in an area that is subject to power cuts or where there is no electricity you can opt for Calor gas heaters. These are used almost exclusively by commercial pheasant producers.

One of the best ways of rearing chicks is under an electric hen. This consumes very little power and mimics a broody hen; it is basically a square or oblong insulated box with an electric heat cable inside which heats a plastic padded cushion on the underside. This box is raised up on adjustable legs and the chicks can creep under it to sleep in the warmth. In general they feather up better with this system and have fewer vices. Always use an electric hen in a heated room or shed.

Rearing boxes

These are normally made of plyboard with a plywood floor, and are 14" to 18" wide (40cms to 45cms), about 36" long (90cms to 100cms) and about 12" high (30cms). There must be room to accomodate the ceramic bulb and shade or the electric hen at one end. You will need a seperate wooden roof for the heated end and small mesh plastic netting to cover the run; roofs are essential as pheasant chicks are great jumpers and soon learn to fly. The floor should be covered with shredded paper to a depth of 0.5" or 1.5cms. Shredded paper has been found to be the best as it is absorbent, it can be burnt or composted easily, and it cannot easily be ingested.

You will need to put in a barrier to prevent the chicks from getting too far into the run at first; make sure you leave enough room for them to feed and drink, and move away from the heat source if they get too warm. As they grow you can gradually move the barrier along the run and take it away completely after a week or ten days; it's important not to let the chicks get wet when they are young as they die very quickly when they are chilled. If you are rearing in a larger area it is essential to corral the chicks near to the heat source as they have a terrible habit of wandering away and dying of cold. Use a long strip of 0.25" hardboard 18" wide (45cms); bend it into a circle and fasten it together with bulldog clips to make a round enclosure. This will ensure that the chicks are never too far away from the heat source and their food and water.

Pheasant chicks can occasionally be shy feeders, and some people like to use egg trays instead of chick crumb feeders for them to start with; if you have this problem try hatching some game bird or guineafowl eggs at the same time as your pheasants and you will find that the game bird or guineafowl chicks will encourage the pheasant chicks to feed.

When introducing your newly hatched youngsters to the rearing box, dip their beaks in water then put them under the heat lamp. They will stagger about a bit at first but will soon become quite nimble. Never mix day old chicks with older ones.

Don't forget, there are always likely to be "dry outs", chicks that don't survive because they live only on their egg sack and die after 3 or 4 days. A sign of this is thin skinny legs.

Once your chicks are over a week old they should be fine barring accidents or bad management. At this stage you will need to clear out the paper litter; clean one end at a time and do it each week from now on. Wash and disinfect the drinkers and provide fresh water daily, not forgetting to add vitamins and probiotics.

A good way to keep your birds healthy is to spray them each day with Virkon S; this also promotes feather growth. As well as this there are new vaccines available now against Newcastle Disease and Avian Flu which are sprayed onto the chicks at day old and taken in through their eyes. Another way to help prevent disease is to line your rearing boxes with plastic sheeting. Fasten this down with drawing pins and then when the batch of birds is moved on, take out the drawing pins and remove the plastic, paper litter, droppings and all. You will need to raise the heat source a little after a week and regularly from then on to help harden off the poults.

Keep an eye on your birds for any signs of toe pecking, shoulder pecking or tail / vent pecking. This can be set off by any number of things: being too hot under the lamp or too stuffy in the shed, thunder, overcrowding, poor quality food, lack of water and sometimes for no apparent reason at all.

Try to keep your birds interested in a good variety of food; for exam-

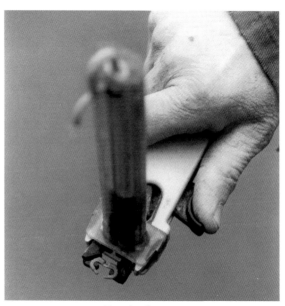

Bit Applicator.

ple, drop a few chopped mealworms or maggots into the box, or offer them some nettles. These are good at stopping your birds from pecking each other: the chicks are stung when they peck the nettles which gives them something else to think about. There are beak bits available on the market, mainly used by commercial pheasant rearers, but they are also useful for young ornamental pheasants if the need arises.

Your poults are ready to be moved on to the rearing pen or seperate arks when they start sleeping away from the raised heat source and have grown all their juvenile feathers.

Rearing pens

To make your rearing pens you will need a number of 10ft (3m) sections; fix these together with plastic ties and use Monaflex to make a reinforced plastic netting roof. This will give your birds some shelter and protect their heads if they become spooked and fly up suddenly. Inside the pens there should be a covered area for a food hopper and drinker, preferably at the end opposite the door. A tip for owners of Koklass pheasants: these birds must be reared on netting floors to keep parasitic worm infections to a minimum. Always set the pens on level ground to prevent escapees, and make sure the grass is kept short both inside and outside. You will need an electric fence to surround the whole area at least 15m away from your birds to protect them from foxes or badgers. After the second day move each pen by a half or quarter of its length, depending on the number of birds inside; this has to be done carefully as it's quite easy to trap the birds' legs or feet if you don't watch what you are doing. The best way is to move first one end and then the opposite one maybe a foot at a time. Don't forget to take away the drinker and

Young White Eared-Pheasants with broodies.

feeder first and put them back when the pen is in the new position.

Place some thick branches or pieces of 2" x "2 across the sections so your birds have somewhere to perch during the day; this will also give them somewhere to get off the wet grass and provide a good vantage point from which to look around.

It is important to keep your poults occupied while they are in the rearing pens: give them supplementary foods, hang up enticing plants like fat hen, nettles or kale to help prevent feather pecking, and look out for mopey birds. This could be a sign of coxy (coccidiosis) and if one or two die have them post mortemed. Always have a couple of empty pens available in case of casualties or bullied birds.

During this time your poults will progress from growers' to adult pellets, the protein level being reduced the older they get. At 12 to 16 weeks you will be able to start sorting them out, putting some into larger holding pens and selling others.

The poults of certain breeds such as Monals, Blood Pheasants, Peacock Pheasants and Argus Pheasants can be housed all together in a larger aviary when they reach about 12 weeks of age.

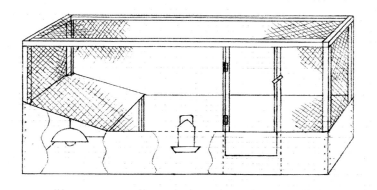

Diagram of a rearing pen.

Handles for moving pen.

Young Brown and Blue Eared-Pheasants. These birds always bred in large numbers, due mainly I believe, to having plenty of room in a spacious aviary.

Young Lineated Kalij and Silver Pheasants.

CATCHING AND TRANSPORTING PHEASANTS

The best way to catch pheasants is to use a medium size dark bag or black cloth landing net. This needs to be about 18" (45cms) across and light weight but strongly made with a handle about 6ft (180cms) long. If the handle is too heavy it will be difficult to wield and if it's too long it will catch on the sides of the aviary. When pheasants are caught like this in a dark bag they will lie still and not struggle.

Stress must be kept to a minimum so speed and care are essential when you are catching pheasants. Their feathers are very loose, a defence mechanism against predators, so always remember to handle a bird by its legs, you don't want to sell one that looks half plucked!

As mentioned in the section on aviary building, it is best to move the required bird from the aviary to the corridor or access area for catching so that the plants in the aviary don't hamper the proceedings.

Pheasants should be transported in cardboard boxes large enough for them to stand up in, with small ventilation holes, and dust free shavings on the floor. If you are using a wooden box it's sometimes advisable to line the inside of the lid with foam rubber to prevent any damage to the birds' heads. Pheasants will travel quite well like this for up to eight hours without food or water.

If you are exporting birds and air-freighting them you will have to make special travelling boxes for them. The boxes must be large enough for a bird to stand up and sit down in, they must have mesh floors to allow liquids and faeces to drop through, and there should be room for feeders and drinkers. The boxes must also be well ventilated and as dark as possible inside. You will need to obtain all the necessary rules and regulations together with flight plans etc. It is quite a military operation but well worth while from the conservation point of view.

It is best to catch the birds in the evening and transport them at night. This causes less stress and means they can travel with a full crop of food.

IDENTIFICATION AND RECORDING

Identification by means of leg rings is an important part of breeding and conservation because it means that whenever you need to, you can obtain information about any individual bird: its age, parentage, fertility and breeding behaviour, when it was last wormed or treated with medication and any susceptibilities to diseases or ailments.

Wing tags are not recommended as they usually cause infections.

There are various kinds of leg ring: metal or plastic, spiral, split or closed. The split ring can be opened to allow the leg to be passed through and then closed with pliers; the closed ring is passed over the young bird's toes and the leg grows to fit it, but ON NO ACCOUNT must the ring be allowed to get too tight. Each type of ring must be able to slide along the leg when in place. Most people use the split rings as the closed ring system can be wasteful.

SELLING PHEASANTS

Providing the breed is not CITES regulated the birds can be sold freely. It is very important to keep a record of your sales so that you know when and where birds have gone and to whom. Records are also important not only to keep a check on numbers of birds kept in captivity, but also as a source of information on blood lines, as in-breeding is a major worry.

With regard to advertising, the best places to aim for are quality local newspapers (which normally have a birds and animals column on Saturdays), the Cage and Aviary Birds newspaper, the World Pheasant Association magazine and the Internet. Once you have been breeding pheasants for a few years and your stock is good you will find that you do not need to advertise so much as word gets round and your reputation spreads. Other breeders will be keen to swap birds or different blood lines with you which is where your record keeping will come into its own. If you are selling pairs of birds you must state whether or not they are related as purchasers will often want unrelated stock.

There are plenty of unscrupulous people out there, especially at markets which I would recommend you avoid if possible. Birds get very stressed in that kind of situation, but if you do go make sure that there is litter in their cages and proper food and water containers for them; they will fetch a better price if they are well presented.

DISEASES AND AILMENTS

We have only attempted to cover the more common diseases that can affect pheasants. If you have a problem it is always advisable to consult your nearest avian vet, and the best way to find one of those is to contact your local zoo, falconry centre or large poultry rearers, and ask them who they use. If you want a post-mortem carried out, take a live bird that has the complaint, not a dead one as they present a different range of complications. Observation is most important: watch for your pheasants taking dust baths, sparring with each other and generally behaving in an alert and lively manner. All these are signs of good health. Droppings should be brown with a white tip. You

A dispenser for administering medications and supplements to plumbed-in drinkers.

should soon see if there is something wrong in a pen by the behaviour of the birds. When you have a number living together it is very easy for a disease to catch hold and spread, sometimes resulting in deaths, unless you are rigorous with your observation and hygiene.

Ensure that there is always clean water and food available and if you introduce different types or makes of food, do it gradually. Always feed the best and freshest food that is well within its sell-by date, make sure that drinkers are washed and disinfected regularly particularly in hot weather, check that the paper litter is dry and that the temperature in the brooder house is at the correct level for the age of birds. If you do all this then you should certainly be able to rear good healthy pheasants.

ASPERGILLOSIS: some breeds such as Argus and Cabot's Tragopans are particularly prone to this disease, and even with the best hygiene will still become infected because they carry it.

Signs - birds stretching their necks to breathe, hoarse breathing noise, dead birds, birds dying within 24 hours.

Cause - a fungus called Aspergillosis fumigatus which is found everywhere but specially in warm damp conditions like wet bedding. A build-up will occur in the litter when a drinker leaks or water is splashed about. Stale food can also be a cause.

Prevention - clean all your rearing equipment and ensure that there is always fresh dry litter. Replace it all if it becomes damp or wet.

Treatment - there is none, just prevention with good management and hygiene.

Mortality - low to medium.

Bio-security. A boot wash outside the entrance to an aviary.

BLACKHEAD (Histomoniasis)

Signs - birds looking listless, uninterested in life or food, losing weight and often with bright yellow diarrhoea.

Cause - Blackhead has nothing to do with the head going black but is a disease of the caecal tracts and liver. It is caused by a minute parasite called Heterakis which is found mainly in the caecal tracts, The eggs of this roundworm carrying the parasite Histomonas, are taken up by the bird and once inside, Histomonas multiplies rapidly, causing severe damage to the caecal tracts and liver, hence the bright yellow droppings. Meanwhile the bird begins to lose weight and interest in life, and eventually dies of blood poisoning due to peritonitis, (the wall of the gut having been pierced). One of the problems with this disease is that the more affected roundworm eggs the birds produce, the worse the situation becomes as the eggs will be passed through more and more birds and worms; this can mean that the disease sometimes remains in the ground for several years. Peacocks are very susceptible to this.

A rat bait box.

Prevention - apart from moving your birds to fresh ground there is none. Treatment - Dimetridazole in the drinking water. Remove all other drinking water and ensure that the birds don't have access to puddles etc. Within 24 hours there should be a marked improvement in them and an interest in food once again. Mortality - low to medium.

COCCIDIOSIS (Coxy)

Signs - milky white diarrhoea sometimes with blood in it, mopey birds, poor growth, thirst, sudden death especially at night. Young stock are particularly vulnerable between 3 to 8 weeks, but this can affect some birds at any age.

Cause - this is a protozoan parasite of which there are many types - 34! The main group is Eimeria of which 10 different kinds occur in pheasants. The Eimeria eggs or oocysts, are passed out in the droppings (an infected bird can produce millions of eggs). They then need warm damp conditions in which to develop, hence Coccidiosis tends to occur more in the Autumn or during periods of wet weather in the summer; it can also be found in damp litter indoors. The eggs or oocysts are picked up by other birds and take up residence in the small intestine, duodenum and caecal tracts where they develop and multiply. The outcome for the bird will depend on the variety or varieties of Coccidiae and the numbers involved. Stress plays a part here too: a low immune system can lead to rapid death.

Prevention - keep the grass in the rearing pens as short as you can. The older the young stock, the greater the immunity they will have, thus it is more often young birds which die of this disease.

Treatment - the most effective treatment is a Sulphadimidine drug like Avatec, but most pheasant foods include a coccidiostat. If in doubt ask your vet about this.

Mortality - can be high.

E-COLI (Colibacillosis)

Signs - in chicks, the bird(s) stands around, often apart from the rest of the group, hunched and cheeping. It is not interested in food or water, and its wings appear too large for its body; there is also a sweet/sour smell. In larger and adult birds E-coli shows itself as birds being off colour, often with runny brown droppings.

Cause - this is a complex set of microbes which normally live harmoniously in the intestines. When poor hygiene, stale food, stress or some other problem like Coccidiosis or Mycoplasma are present, the E-coli bacteria go into overdrive, resulting in the death of the bird, normally from blood poisoning.

Prevention - this is a disease caused by poor management. You must have a thorough programme of cleaning out with a proper disinfectant, not only in the incubator but right the way through the rearing and breeding routine. Stale food, ie out of date food, and stress are other factors involved in E-coli outbreaks.

Treatment - probiotics (Protexin) either in the food or water will clear up

E-coli in chicks, and will work for older birds providing nothing else has latched on such as Coccidiosis or Mycoplasma. If this is the case you may have to treat the other complaint first.

Mortality - low to medium.

MYCOPLASMA, INFECTIOUS SYNOVITIS

Signs - discharge from the nostrils, bubbles in the corner of the eye, scratching the eye area with the foot, wiping infected eye(s) on the base of the neck leaving a 'tide mark' on the feathers, sneezing and rattling, and an awful smell from the bird's nostrils. As the disease worsens, one or both eyes close with a swelling which will harden, under and in front of the eye; this can cause loss of sight in that eye. The bird becomes thinner because it can't see to feed properly. With Infectious synovitis the hock joints swell and the bird has difficulty walking.

Cause - an infectious agent called Mycoplasma gallisepticum and Mycoplasma synoviae. It is spread from bird to bird by sneezing and in the drinking water: this is where automatic drinkers can be a problem. Some birds if not most, seem to be totally immune to the disease, but be aware that it can be transmitted through the egg.

Prevention - always check the stock that you are buying by looking for bubbles in the eyes or swellings at the front of the eyes. Don't forget to do this when you are buying broodies or hens for brooding. Never breed from infected stock and have a good programme of hygiene in place.

Treatment - you can treat this disease with Tylan Soluble or Dicural in the water.

Mortality - normally low.

NEWCASTLE DISEASE OR FOWL PEST

You are unlikely to encounter this disease unless there is a national outbreak which you will hear about anyway. The disease is notifiable which means that, should you think you have the symptoms among your pheasants you must contact your local vet or DEFRA vet immediately.

Signs - these are variable and include necks twisted round, birds flopping about unable to stand, or just twitching. Sometimes there is difficulty in breathing and often a discharge from both ends; egg production will drop also. There can be high mortality or only a few birds dying.

Cause - there are several strains of this virus which is part of the Paramyxovirus group. The different viruses can affect all domestic fowl and some wild birds like sparrows and pigeons, so you can see the potential dangers. The disease attacks the nervous and respiratory systems, hence the lack of co-ordination in the birds. The big worry is that the disease can be spread in so many ways: in the wind, physically on boots, crates, feed bags and vehicles, by wild birds and migrating birds, and also sometimes in egg form but this is considered rare.

Prevention - if there is cause for alarm and the disease is spreading across the country then you can quite simply vaccinate your birds. The treatment is inexpensive but remember that vaccination is not 100% effective although it certainly helps. There are two ways to vaccinate your poults, either through the drinking water or by spraying them with a fine mist which is absorbed through the eye. Adult birds can be injected.

Treatment - there is none and if your birds become infected there will be a mandatory slaughter programme of all the birds in your area.

Mortality - this is of no consequence because if your birds contract the disease you lose everything anyway. In reality mortality can be low and birds do recover from Newcastle Disease, but they are carriers for life having once been infected.

SALMONELLA

There are hundreds of Salmonella bacteria, some more harmful than others.

Signs - with Salmonella typhimurium chicks develop white pasty or blocked up vents. They look miserable and cheep all the time, often standing apart from the others. (You rarely see this with chicks under a broody.)

Cause - in Salmonella typhimurium the bacteria are spread through poor hygiene, stale or infected foodstuffs, dirty nest-boxes, rats and mice or wild birds.

Prevention - in the case of Salmonella typhimurium, you should always check that the chick crumbs and growers pellets are well within the shelf life time limit; also, regular spraying with Virkon S will stop this disease dead in its tracks. It's essential to have an on-going hygiene programme in place from the egg to the poult. This includes thorough cleaning of all equipment used, from incubators, hatchers and brooders to drinkers, feed pans and hoppers.

Treatment - Salmonella typhimurium can be cleared up with the probiotic Protexin. You will have to cull any very sick chicks.

Mortality - medium.

TRICHOMONIASIS AND HEXAMITIASIS

Signs - in young birds 2 to 3 weeks old there is a foamy yellow diarrhoea and acute loss of body weight; you will also notice a nasty sickly smell in the brooder house. When they are older at 7 to 12 weeks, the poults become extremely thin with very prominent breast bones, and sit around for long periods.

Cause - there are two extremely small protozoan parasites, Tricomonas and Hexamita, which are found in the large and small intestines, including the vent and caecal tracts. Large numbers of these parasites are dropped by sickly birds and are easily spread from pen to pen, but neither parasite survives long in a dead body, hence the need to take live sick birds to be post-mortemed.

Prevention - you need to provide fresh rearing ground each year and use footbaths as standard practice.

Treatment - Tetsol, Amoxipen, Amoxicillin.

Mortality - medium to high.

WORMS

Signs - listless birds pecking at food but not really eating, and dead birds as thin as a rake.

Cause - there are many different types of worm which live in, and affect various parts of the digestive system. The most common are the roundworm Hetarakis and the hairworm Capillaria.

Prevention - there is not much you can do to prevent worms as most wild birds live with them. A tip for owners of Koklass pheasants: if you rear these pheasants on netting floors it will help to keep worm infestations to a minimum.

Treatment - Flubenvet (Flubendazole) is a very safe drug which is also used to treat babies in developing countries. It is a fine white powder which you add to the pheasants' food with a little olive oil to help it stick to the pellets or grain. Worm your birds in the Spring, February/March, and again in August/September.

GAPES

This is normally seen in poults from the age of 3 weeks.

Signs - you will hear them coughing and making a noise like 'snick' together with a sideways flick of the head.They open their beaks in a vain attempt to dislodge the culprits.

Life cycle of the Gape Worm

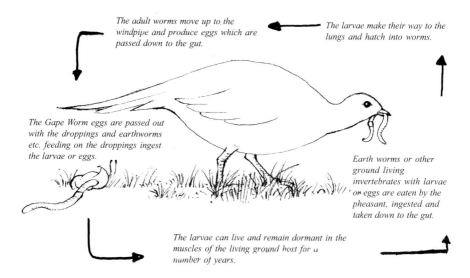

The adult worms move up to the windpipe and produce eggs which are passed down to the gut.

The larvae make their way to the lungs and hatch into worms.

The Gape Worm eggs are passed out with the droppings and earthworms etc. feeding on the droppings ingest the larvae or eggs.

Earth worms or other ground living invertebrates with larvae or eggs are eaten by the pheasant, ingested and taken down to the gut.

The larvae can live and remain dormant in the muscles of the living ground host for a number of years.

Cause - this disease is caused by the roundworm Syngamus trachea. In its adult form it lives in the windpipe of many birds including pheasants and other game birds, and more worryingly wild birds such as starlings and rooks. The flicking of the head is caused by the presence of the worms in the windpipe. The worm is thin and Y shaped and composed of both male and female parts. It produces fertilised eggs which are swallowed by the bird and end up in the droppings. The pheasant, wild bird or game bird either takes this tiny egg from the ground or ingests it via an earthworm which has eaten it. And so the cycle begins again. Death is normally caused by the windpipe becoming blocked with worms. Prevention - fresh rearing ground if possible to prevent outbreaks of Gapes. Note that wild birds can carry this so avoid siting aviaries near a rookery.

Treatment - Gapex, Flubenvet.

Mortality - high in young poults, less as they mature.

FROST BITE

Tropical pheasants like Firebacks can be affected by cold weather even though they cover their feet with their breast feathers while perching.

Signs - black patches appear on the ends of the toes and can extend some way up. After several months the blackened parts will fall off leaving stumps.

Cause - very cold temperatures.

Prevention - it is essential to provide heated quarters 24 hours a day during cold weather. Fixing an off-cut of carpet round the perches will help as well, and is also useful when treating the birds against fleas, mites and lice, as you can can pour the Ban-mite etc onto the carpet where it will soak in and help to protect your pheasants from external parasites.

Treatment - none

Mortality - none; the birds stay healthy but the feet remain sensitive and perching can be a problem.

RED MITE

Signs - none or rarely on the birds. They can look off colour and pale in the face (anaemic). You will see red clusters in perch sockets and cracks and crevices inside the shelter. Young mites are whitish in colour. They are more common in warm weather but can appear at any time.

Cause - Dermanyssus gallinae or Red Mite which lives in crevices and cracks in the shelter and comes out at night to suck the birds' blood. It particularly likes to live in roofing felt which is why you should never use it!

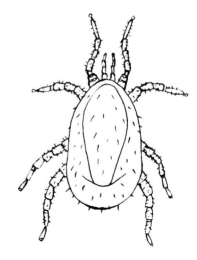

Dermanyssus gallinae
Red Mite.

Prevention - regular cleaning and disinfection of your birds' accomodation.

Treatment - remove any roofing felt if you have any and clean and spray regularly with Duramitex or Ban-mite.

Mortality - deaths can occur with poor management but are uncommon.

SCALEY LEG

Signs - scales lifting up on feet and legs.

Cause - this is caused by a mite called Cnemidocoptes mutans which lives under the scales on the bird's legs and feet. It spreads along the perch from bird to bird.

Prevention - regular cleaning and disinfection of perches and houses.

Treatment - the old fashioned way of dealing with this was to dip the affected leg in a jar of liquid paraffin but today there are quicker and easier methods. Ask your vet for advice on new drugs like Ivomectin.

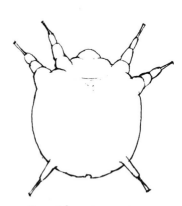

Cnemidocoptes mutans
Scaley Leg Mite.

Mortality - should be nil unless the bird is left without treatment.

CANNIBALISM

Signs - pecked tails, vents, tips of wings, shoulders and toes. Bleeding and death will result. Sometimes the bird's insides are pulled out and eaten leaving an empty carcass.

Cause - mainly stress, too much light when the birds were chicks, over-crowding, lack of food or water, poor quality or stale food, lack of fresh air, stuffy or thundery conditions, or disturbance of any kind.

Prevention - you must check your chicks regularly to make sure all is well. If you catch any in the act of pecking, give them some fresh net-tles; tie bunches and hang them from the roof of the brooder and when the chicks peck them they will get stung and forget about pecking each other. You could also use plastic bits which are fitted into the birds' nostrils to stop the beak from closing completely. Bits are used regularly by breeders of game birds.

Treatment - remove and kill any badly pecked birds; those with slight wounds will need to be sprayed with gentian violet. This turns the wound blue which should deter other birds from pecking it.

CITES

CITES stands for the Convention on International Trade in Endangered Species (of wild flora and fauna). This is an international agreement which controls the movement of certain endangered species throughout most of the world. You will need a permit from CITES to move an endangered species not only in your own country but to anywhere in the world. If you want to buy a breed from an endangered species start by consulting the World Pheasant Association.

And finally, here is an idea for those of you involved with zoos, bird gardens, country parks, or anywhere that is open to the public: you can create a truly spectacular display for your visitors by putting together a collection of male Lady Amherst and Golden Pheasants in an aviary. Do this in the winter before the breeding season starts and when the birds' plumage is at its best, but don't include Reeves Pheasants as they will fight and kill each other. Of course there is nothing to stop you doing this entirely for your own pleasure as well.....

Useful Contacts

World Pheasant Association	ww.pheasant.org.uk
Gamebird and Waterfowl (U.S.A.)	www.gbwf.org
Allandoo Pheasantry	www.allandoopheasantry.com
Brian Moss (Pheasant Breeder)	www.colin-moss@supanet.com
Lindsay Chrisp (Pheasant breeder)	www.pheasants-r-us@tiscali.co.uk
Francy Hermans (Pheasant breeder)	www.tragopan.be
Quails from Wales	www.quailsfromwales.org.uk
The Red House Pheasantry	www.m.vanden.wittenboer@wanadoo.nl

Sara Roadnight

INDEX